Steph King
and
Richard Cooper

TEACHER'S BOOK 1

For more able mathematicians in Year 2

Rising Stars UK Ltd, 7 Hatchers Mews, Bermondsey Street, London SE1 3GS

www.risingstars-uk.com

Published in association with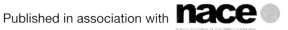

Published 2014
Text, design and layout © Rising Stars UK Ltd. 2014

Authors: Steph King and Richard Cooper
Series Consultant: Cherri Moseley
Text design and typesetting: Mark Walker
Cover design: Lon Chan, Words & Pictures Ltd, London
Publisher: Fiona Lazenby
Editorial: Lynette Woodward and Tom Fryer, Sparks Publishing Services, Ltd
Illustrations: Bill Greenhead (characters), Mark Walker and Steve Evans

British Library Cataloguing in Publication Data.
A CIP record for this book is available from the British Library.

ISBN: 978-1-78339-234-6

Printed by: Ashford Colour Press Ltd

Pages 6–7, TASC: Thinking Actively in a Social Context © Belle Wallace 2004

Contents

Introduction

WELCOME TO THE BRAIN ACADEMY

This series of resources has been developed specifically for the 2014 National Curriculum to support the core aims of ensuring children can reason mathematically and solve problems. The materials are ideal for use with more able children who grasp concepts rapidly to provide extra challenge. The All New Brain Academy missions offer rich and sophisticated problems based around content from the current year's Programme of Study before accelerating into new content from the next year. They draw on mathematics content from across the breadth of the Programme of Study and require children to demonstrate their depth of understanding through a range of increasingly sophisticated challenges that require high-level thinking and perseverance.

HOW TO USE THE PUPIL RESOURCES

Within each Mission File there are 18 missions, each of which requires application of mathematics from different areas of the curriculum, so problems are not restricted to one topic. For example, a Mission File may include elements of number, geometry, measurement and statistics and require children to make connections between these areas of mathematics.

The problems can be set so children work on their own, in pairs or in small groups in the mathematics classroom. Working with others will support some of the language demands of the contexts and questions, as well as encouraging collaboration and the use of mathematical vocabulary. The resources also work well for homework or as the focus of a club.

Children should be encouraged to discuss the problems with others and consider different strategies that could be used that provide either a specific or a generic application. For example, making a list is a generic example that will help to develop a systematic approach.

The use of practical resources should be promoted as these can support children in making sense of more complex contexts and provide a visual representation of the problem. Calculators are a useful tool to help children investigate more extensively, especially with more complicated calculations, where the problem solving itself would be impeded by the time required to complete written procedures.

As teachers, we need to model how to take risks and how to be a problem solver. You may find that participating as a problem solver in the group encourages the children to communicate their ideas more effectively and adopt some of the strategies that you apply.

Information will be presented in a variety of forms including tables, charts, graphs, timetables, scales, clocks, geometrical diagrams, and so on.

The introduction to each Mission sets the scene for the problems that the children will need to solve.

The Main Mission (MM) presents more sophisticated problems which may draw on logic, visual problems, patterns and rules, etc. Again, children are required to interpret information represented in different ways.

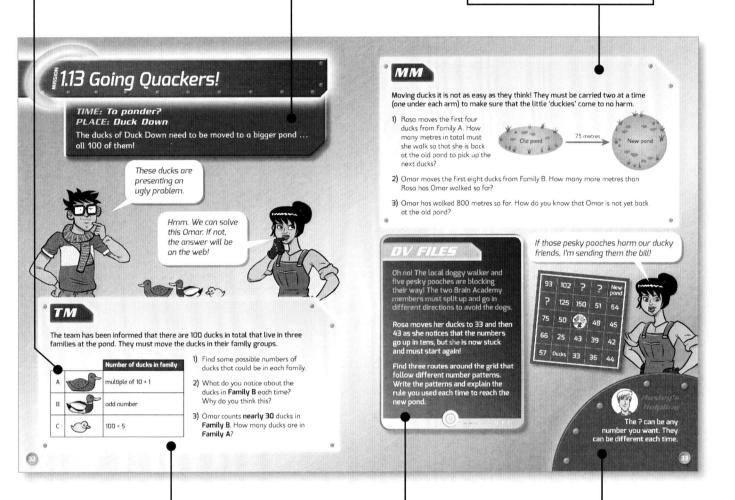

The Training Mission (TM) requires children to use the information given and apply their mathematical knowledge and skills. They will need to reason and explain, thus demonstrating their mathematical fluency.

The Da Vinci Files (DV Files) raise the challenge further and provide a set of more non-routine problems with a greater degree of sophistication. These work well as group tasks to continue to develop reasoning and problem-solving strategies.

Huxley's Helpline reminds the children of vital information or provides hints for how an answer should be presented, for example round all measurements to the nearest whole centimetre. Suggestions are also made to support the process of problem solving, for example record your solutions in a table to help you identify patterns.

PROBLEM-SOLVING STRATEGIES

At the back of each of the Mission Files, children will find some further support in the form of Mission Strategies. These are designed to scaffold the problem-solving process to develop skills generally, in addition to providing specific hints and ideas as starting points for each mission if children find it difficult to make progress.

The TASC Problem Solving Wheel (TASC: Thinking Actively in a Social Context ©Belle Wallace 2004) provides a set of strategies to encourage children to think actively by gathering information, identifying the problem and making a number of decisions about methods and effective ways to communicate ideas. These strategies form valuable discussion points for the teacher and children as some aspects are likely to require further development than others. These are likely to be different for each individual.

Teachers and other adults will find it useful to model some of these processes so that children are clear about each step and, over time, learn to be expert thinkers! In particular, you may find that your more able pupils need to further develop strategies to evaluate, communicate and reflect on their thinking. They should always be encouraged to look for more than one solution and different ways to solve problems.

In addition to the Huxley's Helpline clue within each mission, the children will find a further set of strategies to support each of the challenges. These Mission Strategies may refer to the Training Mission (TM), the Main Mission (MM) or the Da Vinci Files (DV FILES).

The strategies have a range of different purposes. For example, they may be:

- A reminder about valuable pieces of information that may need to be referred to in more than one mission. This is to prompt children to think about what they already know.

- A reference to a conversion that they will need to apply or to the properties of 2-D and 3-D shapes. This is to remind children to draw upon their mathematical knowledge and skills.

- A suggestion of a starting point or a systematic approach. This provides some generic ideas that can be used to solve other problems.

- A recommendation of a way to record or present ideas so that patterns can be identified and any missing solutions found. This provides children with a model to organise their ideas and communicate their thinking.

Children should be encouraged to have a go at the problem first, before referring to the Mission Strategies for help. This will provide a clear picture of what children can do and what skills they can apply independently.

TASC WHEEL

TASC stands for Thinking Actively in a Social Context. Developed by Belle Wallace, Past President of NACE, TASC is a well-researched universal thinking skills framework which empowers learners to:

- work independently yet within an inclusive school policy
- develop skills of research, investigation and problem-solving that can be used across the curriculum
- develop a positive sense of self as an active learner
- develop their abilities using the full range of multiple intelligences
- develop skills of self-assessment.

TASC provides teachers with a framework for:

- lesson planning that systematically develops pupils' thinking and personalises their learning
- effective planning for differentiation and extension
- a holistic approach to incorporating the full range of human abilities
- assessing the processes of pupils' learning.

The TASC Wheel represents a series of thinking skills that an expert thinker uses. An expert has automatised these processes and uses them flexibly, flipping forwards and backwards as the task demands. Very often, teachers are using these processes in their planning and delivery, but they do not usually share their thinking processes with the pupils.

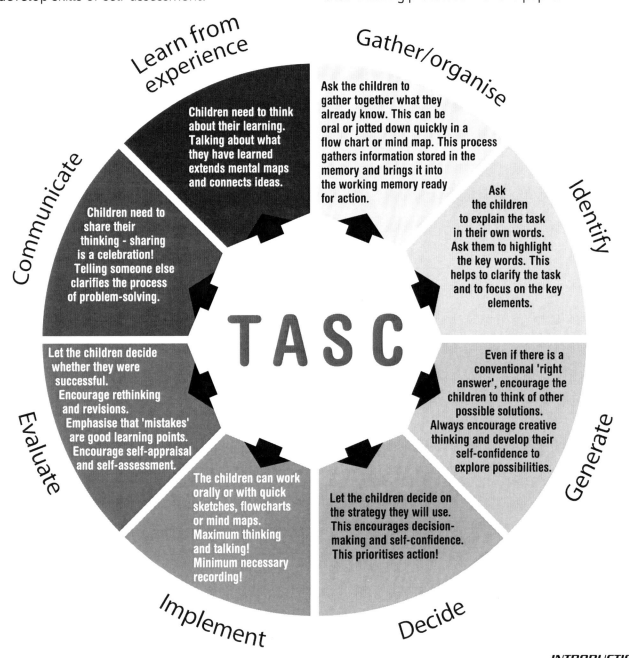

The *All New Brain Academy* Teacher's Books provide the background information needed to summarise each of the problems in the corresponding Mission File, along with a full set of answers and worked examples. The mathematical content for each mission is clearly identified and draws from all areas of the National Curriculum.

All New Brain Academy provides valuable opportunities to assess the depth of children's understanding and the range of strategies they use. For each mission you will find examples of strategies to look out for and any misconceptions that may arise. There may also be suggestions that could be made to help children access the tasks if they are finding it difficult to identify a starting point or keep track of the information or results.

All the challenges draw upon different types of problem solving. These are:

- Finding all possibilities
- Logic problems
- Finding rules and describing patterns
- Diagram problems and visual puzzles
- Word problems (one-, two- or multi-step)

Examples of the first four types in the list above are as follows:

Finding all possibilities	Logic problems
• Finding different possible amounts • Finding different ways to get to an amount • Combinations • Permutations • Finding missing numbers	• Magic squares • Connected clues • Sudoku • Meeting more than one criterion
Finding rules and describing patterns	**Diagram problems and visual puzzles**
• Sequences • Graphs • Determining values that meet a rule	• Identifying shapes hidden in a diagram • Identifying missing angles or lengths of sides • Mazes

These problem-solving types or examples are not listed under the mathematical content in each mission as the majority of the challenges involve a combination of all types of problem-solving. There are also no direct references to reasoning as, like problem solving, this is integral to all missions.

The Mathematical Content refers to broad themes within the curriculum. Each mission draws on a range of areas and is not focused on one particular objective or topic.

Each problem is summarised and provides a useful insight into possible strategies, assessment opportunities, ways to support the children, and so on. Sometimes a useful model is also provided.

MISSION 1.13 Going Quackers!

MATHEMATICAL CONTENT

- Odd numbers
- Multiples of 10
- Division
- Distance (metres)
- Addition and subtraction
- Place value
- Number facts (including bonds to 100)
- Sequences

TEACHING NOTES

TM

The mission focuses on the safe transport of three families of ducks to a new pond elsewhere in the village.

The children must first identify the number of ducks that live in these large families. They are told that there are 100 ducks altogether, but then are given clues to help find the exact number in each family.

Children draw on knowledge of number bonds to 100, odd numbers, division and patterns found in numbers that are all one more than a multiple of 10.

A final clue that reveals that there are nearly 30 in one of the families helps the children to identify the solution from the possible set of solutions that they have so far.

MM

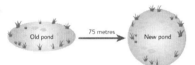

Old pond — 75 metres → New pond

The key facts here are that only two ducks can be carried at a time and 75 m is the distance of a one-way journey to the new pond. Omar and Rosa must always walk a further 75 m each time to return to the old pond to collect the next pair of ducks.

Using knowledge of doubles, children should identify that as Omar has carried twice as many ducks, he must have walked twice as far. The difference is, therefore, 300 m.

Look for children who recognise that all complete journeys are lots of 150 m and can use this to explain why Omar, having walked 800 m, is not yet back at the old pond. He still has 100 m left to go.

TEACHING NOTES

DV FILES

To complete the mission, the children must help Rosa find her way around a group of dogs that are out on a walk.

The grid is filled with sets of numbers that create patterns (sequences). In order to avoid the dogs, Rosa must follow suggested patterns to get to the new pond.

The children must identify patterns and provide the rule that they have used.

93	102	?	?	New pond
?	125	150	51	54
75	50	🐕	48	45
66	25	43	39	42
57	Ducks	33	36	44

Several question marks can also be found in the grid so that they can be used in different ways to help complete each sequence.

Look for the strategies children use when adding 9 each time to complete the sequence 57, 66, 75, 84, 93, 102, etc. or any explanations they may use for simply continuing the pattern of ascending tens and descending units or ones until zero is reached (120 in this case).

ANSWERS

TM

1)

A	11	21	31	41	51	61	71
B	69	59	49	39	29	19	9
C	20	20	20	20	20	20	20

2) The number of ducks in Family B all have 9 units or ones. The 9 must go with the 1 from Family A to make another ten as the total needed (80) is a multiple of 10.

3) 29 Family B so Family A must be 51.

MM

1) 300 m
2) 300 m
3) It takes 150 m to go to the new pond and back. We know that 600 m is walked for eight ducks, another 150 m for another two ducks and then only 50 m is left to make up 800 m. This is not enough to get to the new pond and back again. Children may also explain that, after 600 m, the next time Omar is back at the old post is after 750 m and then after 900 m so he could not be back there after 800 m.

DV FILES

Route 1: Add 3 each time or multiples of 3
33, 36, 39, 42, 45, 48, 51, 54
Route 2: Add 25 each time or multiples of 25
25, 50, 75, 100, 125, 150, 175, 200
Route 3: Add 9 each time
57, 66, 75, 84, 93, 102, 111, 120

The notes may also provide a way into the problem and identify the key piece of information that should be used or is pivotal to finding a solution.

All missions come with a full set of solutions. More complicated questions or problems are accompanied by worked examples and further explanations or guidance.

MATHEMATICAL CONTENT

- Properties of 2-D shapes
- Addition and subtraction
- Multiplication
- Length (cm)
- Equivalence
- Number bonds

TEACHING NOTES

TM This mission requires the children to identify a set of 2-D shapes from the information they are given about their properties. In two cases (triangles), the number of sides is the same so they will need to consider another given property to help make a final decision.

It may be useful for children to have access to a set of shapes if they are unsure, but initially the task will be a valuable assessment opportunity if they have to reason first before checking.

The second question requires the children to consider a possible question that could be asked to distinguish between a square and a rectangle.

MM The length of only one side is given for each of the two kites in the Main Mission. Children should recognise that both the pentagon and equilateral triangle have sides of equal length. They may already know the term 'regular', although this is not expected at Key Stage 1. Knowing that all sides of the shape are, say, 42 cm in the case of the pentagon, will help them calculate the total wood needed for all sides.

Look for children who may already employ a method of multiplication using partitioning in some way or use known facts, e.g. knowing double 75 and then adding one more 75.

Children are also likely to use a method of repeated addition. This may use partitioning, jumps on a number line or even a vertical column method.

Again, look for the way that children carry out the subtraction 225 cm − 210 cm. Do they recognise that they can simply find the difference by counting on from 210 cm?

DV FILES

This puzzle is an adaptation of the Magic Square. The children are given the total required for the rows and the diagonals and must try out different permutations in the 3 × 3 grid to find a possible solution.

As with other Magic Squares, solutions can be reflected or rotated as long as the numbers in the rows or diagonals stay together.

Children may find it useful to sketch a grid and move the shapes around it until a solution is found.

ANSWERS

TM

1)

Straight sides	Curved sides	Right angles	Name
4	0	4	rectangle or square
3	0	1	right-angled triangle
5	0	0	pentagon
1	1	0	semicircle
3	0	0	any triangle without a right angle

2) E.g. 'Are the sides all equal in length?' or similar.

MM

1) Kite A   42 cm × 5 = 210 cm
   Kite B   75 cm × 3 = 225 cm
   Kite B uses more wood.

2) 15 cm more wood.

DV FILES

Rows sum to 13 and diagonals to 11.
E.g.

4	6	3
4	5	4
3	8	2

or

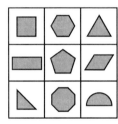

1.2 Feeling A Bit Drained?

MATHEMATICAL CONTENT

- Counting in steps of twos, threes and fives
- Equivalence
- Temperature
- Time
- Negative numbers in a context
- Place value
- Partitioning in different ways

TEACHING NOTES

TM The Training Mission is focused upon identifying the number of trapped children on a school visit.

Limited information has been provided, but the clues require counting in steps of two, threes and then fives.

It is key that children recognise the numbers that appear in more than one count, e.g. 12 appearing in both the counts of two and three. Look for children who also spot that these are the numbers found when counting in sixes from zero. Ask questions to deepen their understanding so that they know why this is the case.

This can be supported with visuals, e.g. integer bars or Cuisenaire Rods.

Later, possible numbers of children are eliminated as we find out that the group was also counted in fives. This leaves us with 30, 60 etc. as the only solutions. However, it is revealed that all the children came on one coach that holds a maximum of 55 people. The solution can now be found.

MM Children apply knowledge of counting in twos to a scale (thermometer) with intervals of two. Although the problem does not require children to work with them, negative values also appear here in context.

The problem requires the tracking of temperature as it drops by 2 °C every half hour. The time when the temperature reaches the value shown on the scale must also be determined.

DV FILES

Knowledge of place value and partitioning in different ways is key to solving the last problem.

Each digit on the display must be reset to zero following two subtractions.

Children should be encouraged to find a range of subtractions and explain why each is possible.

Look for children who consider the 9, 7 and 6 as only single digits and so find it difficult to come up with a range of possibilities where the place value is essential, e.g. as required for 900 in Question 3.

ANSWERS

TM

1) Multiples of both two and three children are possible. This means:
6, 12, 18, 24, 30, 36, 42, 48, 54

2) 30

3) Agree, because we know that there is a maximum number of 55 children on the coach. After 30, the next number that works for all counts is 60, but that is more than 55. So there must be 30 children on the trip.

MM

1)

11 o'clock	Half past 11	12 o'clock	Half past 12	1 o'clock	Half past 1
19 °C	17 °C	15 °C	13 °C	11 °C	9 °C

2) Half past two (2:30).

DV FILES

1) 60 then 10, 10 then 60, 50 then 20, 20 then 50, 30 then 40 or 40 then 30.

2)

Control Panel

9   7   6

900 then 0		6 then 0
0 then 900		0 then 6
		5 then 1
800 then 100		1 then 5
100 then 800		4 then 2
700 then 200		2 then 4
200 then 700		3 then 3
600 then 300		
300 then 600		
500 then 400		
400 then 500		
Or, for example:		
850 then 50		

3) Yes, because 350 + 550 = 900, so Huxley has still subtracted 900 in total.

MATHEMATICAL CONTENT

- Right angles
- Clockwise and anti-clockwise turns
- Understanding the =, < and > sign
- Fractions of sets or amounts
- Length (cm and m)
- Doubling and halving
- Counting in steps of 50
- Equivalence

TEACHING NOTES

The shortest route through the maze should be found to solve this problem. Children will have to measure accurately and make comparisons. Look out for children who automatically measure from the end of the ruler rather than locating zero.

The number of clockwise and anti-clockwise turns must also be counted and compared.

Children should be encouraged to turn the image to check the directions of turns that appear in a less familiar orientation.

Check the children's understanding of the > sign and recognising that the number of turns are equal.

There is often a misconception that the = sign means 'makes' or indicates that an answer will follow.

This is not true. Children should be able to explain that 'equals' means that each side of the number sentence has the same (equal) value but may not look the same, e.g.

$8 = 8$ or $8 = 6 + 2$ **or** $9 - 1 = 6 + 2$ etc.

The ball pit already holds a number of different coloured balls, which could make the task a little trickier.

Rather than being asked to find, say $\frac{1}{2}$ of 24, children are required to recognise that the 12 blue balls represent half of 24. The fraction is not given.

The problem then develops so that we are told the fraction and the amount it represents but we are not told the value of the whole, e.g.

$\frac{1}{4}$ of _____ red balls = 9 balls

Language structures and resources can also support here to secure understanding where necessary, e.g. cubes, integer bars, Cuisenaire or Numicon.

Quarters means 4 equal parts and each quarter is worth 9

TEACHING NOTES

The children are required to reason and prove Gammon's thinking by showing a worked example or giving an explanation.

They should draw upon knowledge that there are 100 cm in a metre and that there are four lots of 25 in 100, or 25 goes into 100 four times. This will inform their decision about the length of wood needed for the steps.

The final problem challenges the children to consider different possible lengths of Rope A that are multiples of 50 cm and recognise that Robe B must be double the length each time.

It is important from an early stage that children recognise that there may be more than one solution.

ANSWERS

TM

1) See route in answer for Question 3 — children's own recording.
   Approximately 15 cm
2) 8 right angle turns.
3) *CW turns = ACW turns*
   CW = clockwise turn
   ACW = anticlockwise turn

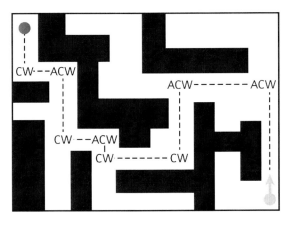

MM

1) Blue $\frac{1}{2}$ of 24 balls = 12 balls,
   Yellow $\frac{1}{4}$ of 24 balls = 6 balls.
2) 36 red balls and 45 green balls in a full bag.

DV FILES

1) For each ladder they need 4 m of wood for the sides, so 8 m in total for two ladders. There are 100 cm in a metre so four steps can be made from a metre of wood. 2 m are needed for the eight steps for one ladder, so 4 metres are needed for two ladders.

2) E.g. children's own recording, but it would be valuable to look at the use of a table to record possibilities.

Rope A	50 cm	100 cm	150 cm	200 cm	250 cm
Rope B	100 cm	200 cm	300 cm	400 cm	500 cm

MATHEMATICAL CONTENT

- Mass
- Capacity
- Multiplication and division
- Height (cm and m)
- Subtraction as difference
- Length (m)

TEACHING NOTES

 A table of facts must be completed in this mission. The children are given the amount of food and water needed by the giraffe each day and must find out how much is needed after 2 days, 3 days etc.

Look for children who use doubling to find 2 days and, perhaps, double this again for 4 days. They may also use multiplication facts and partitioning or the strategy of repeated addition to support multiplication.

Rosa's mistake in Question 2 is a typical error with division. Look for children who can explain that the value that goes first in the calculation is the amount to be shared (sharing model) or to have groups subtracted from it (grouping model).

 The key knowledge needed in this mission is that there are 100 cm in a metre. Once this is identified, the children should compare heights and use a model of subtraction to help find the difference.

You will notice that the language varies throughout the mission, i.e. write the difference or how much taller.

Look for use of the words 'shorter' and 'taller' when comparing heights rather than 'bigger' and 'smaller'.

DV FILES

The final mission is an investigation to find different possible routes around the town that can be used to return the giraffe to the zoo. All distances are multiples of 5 m.

Look for children who make use of number bonds and place values when adding values, e.g. when adding 40 m and 50 m use number bonds for 4 add 5 to help. Children in Year 2 also use known bonds to derive related bonds to 100. Again, look for application of these strategies rather than children using column methods here.

ANSWERS

TM

1)

	1 day	2 days	3 days	4 days
Food	44 kg	88 kg	132 kg	176 kg
Water	35 litres	70 litres	105 litres	140 litres

2) E.g. Rosa has written the calculation in the wrong order. She needs to start with 175 litres as this is the total for 5 days, and then divide by 5 to check that the answer shows that the giraffe drinks 35 litres each day.

MM

1) Lamp post is 150 cm taller or giraffe is 150 cm shorter.

2) Tree is 4 m taller or giraffe is 4 m shorter.

3) The giraffe is 415 cm taller.

DV FILES

1) Children's own route.

2)

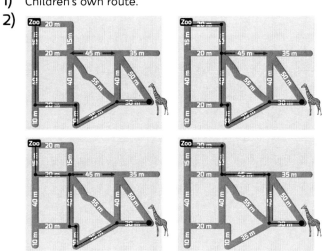

1.5 Art Attack!

MATHEMATICAL CONTENT

- Identifying 2-D shapes
- Length (cm)
- Multiplication
- Addition
- Place value

TEACHING NOTES

TM The Training Mission requires children to identify a range of 2-D shapes from a painting, including a parallelogram and a trapezium. Many of these shapes overlap or are actually formed by an overlap. This makes the task more visually challenging.

Children are also introduced to irregular polygons in this mission, although they may not yet know the terms 'regular' and 'irregular'. It is important that the shapes themselves are determined by the number of straight sides (and, therefore, vertices) that form the closed shape rather than the more familiar images they will have seen. Resources tend to include regular pentagons, hexagons and octagons.

MM The Main Mission focuses on finding the lengths of wood needed to frame two different-shaped pictures. This will later pave the way for work on perimeter.

Children should recognise that rectangles have two pairs of sides of equal length, whereas the hexagon shown has six sides of equal length.

Look for the strategies children use to find totals, e.g. methods of doubling, partitioning, multiplication or repeated addition. Children may already know double 75 or double 45. The hexagon purposely has sides of 30 cm to encourage the children to use some of the work they have done on counting in threes and applying it to counting in steps of 30.

Look for children who recognise that these calculations can be written using the multiplication sign, e.g.

30 cm × 6 and for Question 3, 20 × 6.

TEACHING NOTES

The Da Vinci mission is all about permutations. Children are encouraged to think about using a code for each of the pictures to help their recording.

Look for strategies the children use to keep track of each possibility and recognise any repetitions.

If they have missed several solutions, look together at ways of being systematic, e.g. finding all the possibilities where the shape picture is first.

They should notice that there are four sets of six possibilities, each set keeping one picture at the front and moving the other three. It may be interesting to ask them to predict what would have happened had there had been only three pictures to order.

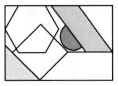

| Shapes | Flowers | Portrait |

SFP   FSP   PSF
SPF   FPS   PFS

Far fewer possibilities than the children might expect!

ANSWERS

TM

1) E.g. semi-circle, triangle, right-angled triangle, square, trapezium, parallelogram, hexagon.
2) Pentagon, because it has five sides.
3)

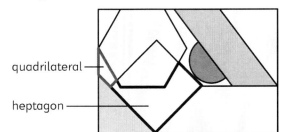

quadrilateral

heptagon

MM

1) 240 cm
2) 180 cm
3) 20 × 6 = 120 pieces

DV FILES

1)	SFPR	13)	PSFR
2)	SFRP	14)	PSRF
3)	SPFR	15)	PRSF
4)	SPRF	16)	PRFS
5)	SRPF	17)	PFRS
6)	SRFP	18)	PFSR
7)	FSPR	19)	RSFP
8)	FSRP	20)	RSPF
9)	FRSP	21)	RPSF
10)	FRPS	22)	RPFS
11)	FPRS	23)	RFPS
12)	FPSR	24)	RFSP

There are 24 in total

MATHEMATICAL CONTENT

- Turns — clockwise and anti-clockwise, fractions of a turn
- Position and direction
- Place value
- Ordering 3-digit numbers
- Properties of 3-D shapes
- Statistics (Venn Diagram)

TEACHING NOTES

TM

In the Training Mission, the team must be given instructions to direct them around a seaside town.

Children are asked to use 'F' for 'Forward' and describe turns as fractions of a whole turn. They must also decide whether this turn should be clockwise or anti-clockwise.

The last question requires them to reason about the equivalence of $\frac{3}{4}$ of a turn anti-clockwise and $\frac{1}{4}$ of a turn clockwise.

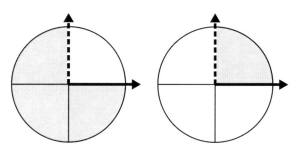

MM

The Brain Academy team need to find the code to unlock the treasure chest. The children must find all possible codes using the digits 2, 0 and 3. The zero has been used to reinforce the effect on the size of the number when it is placed in the hundreds position, i.e. it now becomes a number less than 100 in this case. This will be key when writing each of the numbers in words. However, the codes for the padlock will still require the zero in this position, e.g. 023.

The six numbers must be ordered from smallest to largest and finally 180 should be subtracted from 203 to find the correct solution. Look for methods that children use to subtract 180, as although subtracting 100 is straightforward, they will have to cross the hundreds boundary in order to subtract 80.

Children are likely to use a sketched number line to count back 80 either as tens or groups of ten. They should be able to spot any errors using what they know about the value of the units or ones digit when counting in tens (not crossing zero).

DV FILES

The Da Vinci mission uses a Venn Diagram in the context of a 3-D shape. Having been given two properties, the children must use the Venn Diagram to help identify the four solid shapes that have been found in the chest.

Huxley's Helpline reminds the children that they can make use of a set of shapes in the classroom to help make decisions.

The key to this mission is recognising that the labels do not say 'Only △ faces' or 'Only ▭ faces'.

This gives further possibilities and helps children to reason why Shape C can be a hexagonal prism and identify possibilities for Shape D.

ANSWERS

TM

1) F, $\frac{1}{4}$ turn clockwise, F, $\frac{1}{4}$ turn anticlockwise, F, $\frac{1}{4}$ turn anticlockwise, F, $\frac{1}{4}$ turn clockwise, F.

2) Because it would be easier to make a $\frac{1}{4}$ turn CW as it is the same as $\frac{3}{4}$ turn ACW.

MM

1) 203, 230, 023, 032, 302, 320
   Two hundred and three, two hundred and thirty, twenty three, thirty two, three hundred and two, three hundred and twenty.

2) 23, 32, 203, 230, 302, 320

3) 1240

DV FILES

1) Shape A: tetrahedron or a square based pyramid (as it does not say that it only has triangular faces).
   Shape B: triangular prism or rectangular-based pyramid..
   Shape C: cuboid (or another prism, e.g. hexagonal as this has rectangular faces and it does not say only).
   Shape D: sphere, cone, cube, cylinder.

2) Yes, it could be as it has six rectangular faces. It also has two hexagonal faces, but the label does not say 'only rectangular faces'.

1.7 Star Spotting!

MATHEMATICAL CONTENT

- Place value
- Subtraction (difference)
- Time — days and weeks (including conversion)
- Symmetry
- Multiplying and dividing by 10
- Distance (km)

TEACHING NOTES

TM Understanding of place value is required here so that the value of each digit 6 can be identified, the value of 6 for the planet Neptune being the most challenging.

The difference between the number of days taken to orbit the Sun by Earth and Venus should be quickly identified as being a multiple of 10 days as both contain the digit 5 in the units or ones position.

Children should draw upon knowledge that there are 7 days in a week and that 88 is more than 10 groups of 7 (70) or 7 groups of ten (70).

Planet	Approximate number of days
Mercury	88
Venus	225
Earth	365
Mars	687
Jupiter	4333
Saturn	10,759
Uranus	30,684
Neptune	60,190
Pluto (dwarf planet)	90,465

MM The Main Mission focuses on symmetrical patterns and asks the children to explain why the image seen through the telescope is or is not symmetrical. The line of symmetry is vertical. A mirror would be useful to reinforce the effects of symmetry, including the fact that any shapes or objects reflected do not change their shape or size, although they will have 'flipped'.

With the arrival of two more objects, the children should decide where they should go to make the pattern symmetrical. Children should use a mirror to confirm their solution.

TEACHING NOTES

DV FILES

The Da Vinci mission makes the effect of multiplication and division explicit as the distances are scaled up or down by 10. The inverse is key to help the children make sense of when they need to multiply and when they need to divide depending on the information they have been given.

Numbers are extended to include thousands. All examples are in the context of kilometres.

Place value grids will be useful here to reinforce or simply to check.

Th	H	T	U or O	
	1	5	0	÷ 10
		1	5	
	2	3	0	x 10
2	3	0	0	

ANSWERS

TM

1)
Earth	60
Mars	600
Uranus	600
Neptune	60,000
Pluto	60

2) 140 days

3) There are 7 days in a week so 10 weeks is 70 days. It takes Mercury 88 days, which is more than 70 days.

MM

1) It is not symmetrical because A and B are not symmetrical. C and D are symmetrical in the yellow mirror line, as are E and F.

2)

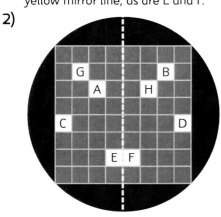

Or G and H can be swapped.

DV FILES

1)

	Real distance (km)	With telescope (km)
Object A	150	**15**
Object B	**2300**	230
Object C	950	**95**
Object D	**180**	18

150 km ÷ 10 = 15 km

230 km × 10 = 2300 km

950 km ÷ 10 = 95 km

18 km × 10 = 180 km

2) E.g. any distances as long as the real distance is 10 times further than through the telescope.

	Real distance (km)	With telescope (km)
Object E	1400	140
Object F	1000	100
Object G	850	8
Object H	990	99

1.8 Rocking Horse Runaways

MISSION

MATHEMATICAL CONTENT

- Counting in steps of three and four
- Statistics (bar chart)
- Addition and subtraction (including difference)

TEACHING NOTES

 The children are provided with an incomplete bar chart showing the number of rocking horses that have escaped from neighbouring streets.

The scale of the chart is in fours, but some values are on unlabelled points.

The term 'half-way' is used to help find the number of rocking horses that escaped from Stallion Hill.

Children must also make comparisons by finding the difference and find the total number of runaways.

This mission focuses on counting on, either to find the difference or to find the house number of the seventh rocking horse.

Look for children who use knowledge of number facts or sketch number lines. Particularly look at the sizes of jumps used, e.g. multiples of 10 recognising that the units or ones digit remains the same, using bonds to 10 to reach the next multiple of 10, etc.

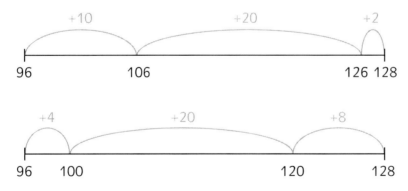

DV FILES

The children must break a code in this final mission. They are encouraged to write out the alphabet to help them keep track of the values that have been assigned to each letter.

However, they must first identify that the sequence is going up in steps of three, but must apply this to the alphabet written in reverse order.

57	36	27	24	66	24		24	57	36	18	45	69		75	66		63	27	66	66	.
36	63	63		21	36		21	57	66		33	78	27	48	!						

ANSWERS

TM

1) 10 more.
2) 20 rocking horses at Stallion Hill.
3) 20 + 18 + 22 + 12 = 72 in total.

MM

1) 24 houses

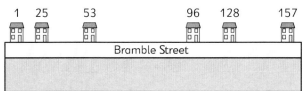

Bramble Street

2) 25 to 53 is 28 houses
   53 to 96 is 43 houses
   96 to 128 is 32 houses
   128 to 157 is 29 houses
3) 261

DV FILES

The clue is 'Horses should be free. Off to the park!'

MATHEMATICAL CONTENT

- Mass
- Equivalence
- Fractions (equivalence)
- Fractions of sets or amounts

- Multiplication and division
- Addition
- Arrays

TEACHING NOTES

The missions revolve around the team having to save Stonehenge from a plague of moles.

The Training Mission shows the mass of soil the moles are digging from beneath it and how they are transporting it out of the tunnels.

We are told that a maximum of 14 kg can be taken in one trip, although the moles have the option to carry a half-load. Initially, children are given the number of full or half loads so the total mass each time can be found.

However, for the fourth trip, the children must find different combinations of half loads and full loads to total the 56 kg mass carried. They should use and reason about what they already know from the first tunnels rather than recalculating each time or randomly trying things out, e.g.

'I know that 42 kg was 3 full loads in the first tunnel and 56 kg is 14 kg more. So 4 full loads is a possible solution.'

They should also recognise that there are two half loads in every full load and so further possibilities can be found by simple exchanging each full load for two half loads.

The number of moles in each team is shown as an array. Children should be used to working with arrays in the classroom and be able to explain how they are structured.

Look for children who make use of the structure of the arrays to count in groups or are able to recognise what it represents because of the related multiplication fact. Children should not be counting the whole array in ones.

The mission requires the related multiplication fact to be written. Children may also use the commutative law to write down more than one fact, i.e.

8×5 and 5×8.

The final team of moles has 36 members. Different possible arrays should be described.

A final total of moles can then be found.

DV FILES

The children should use the totals found for teams A, B and C in the previous mission to help complete the Da Vinci problem.

Simple fractions, i.e. $\frac{1}{2}$, $\frac{1}{3}$, $\frac{1}{4}$ and $\frac{3}{4}$ of these totals should be found so that the number of moles that followed Huxley can be determined.

Fraction bars are a useful image to help secure or confirm fractions of amounts, e.g. $\frac{1}{3}$ of 21 = 7.

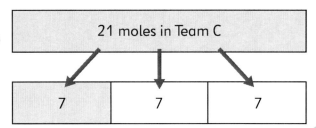

ANSWERS

TM

1)

	Number of full loads	Number of half loads	kg of soil moved
First tunnel	3	0	42 kg
Second tunnel	5	1	77 kg
Third tunnel	5	2	84 kg
Fourth tunnel	e.g. 4	0	56 kg

2)

Fourth tunnel	4	0	56 kg
	3	2	56 kg
	2	4	56 kg
	1	6	56 kg
	0	8	56 kg

MM

1) A = 24 moles, B = 40 moles, C = 21 moles.
2) A **6 × 4** (or 4 × 6 looking at columns first);
   B **8 × 5** (or 5 × 8 looking at columns first);
   C **7 × 3** (or 3 × 7 looking at columns first).
3) E.g. 1 row of 36, 2 rows of 18, 3 rows of 12, 4 rows of 9, 6 rows of 6, etc.
4) 24 + 40 + 21 + 36 = 121 moles.

DV FILES

1)

	Total number of moles	Fraction of moles that followed Mason	Fraction of moles that followed Evan	Number of moles that followed Hux
Team A	24	$\frac{1}{4}$	$\frac{1}{3}$	10
Team B	40	$\frac{1}{4}$	$\frac{3}{4}$	0
Team C	21	$\frac{1}{3}$	$\frac{1}{3}$	7
Team D	36	$\frac{1}{2}$	$\frac{1}{3}$	6

1.10 Sweetie Beans

MATHEMATICAL CONTENT

- Time
- Capacity (ml)
- Reading scales
- Height (cm)
- Money

TEACHING NOTES

TM The Training Mission firstly requires the children read three analogue clocks and write the times in words. They must then find the difference between a morning and afternoon time by calculating the interval. Look for children who make use of a resource clock or sketch a number line to support the calculation. This can also be suggested as a strategy to those who are unsure.

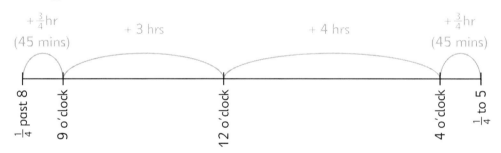

The problem develops to include capacity marked on a scale with intervals of 25 ml but labels in 50 ml.

The value should be read from the scale and multiplied by 3 to find the total amount of water used in a day.

MM The Main Mission shows the familiar scale on a ruler. The picture shows the height of the plant on Day 9, and the children must use the information to find its height on the previous and subsequent days. The measurements here include whole and half centimetres.

Question 3 asks the children to find out when the plant reaches $26\frac{1}{2}$ cm. Look for children who recognise that the plant grows 7 cm every 2 days and use this to find the solution more efficiently.

TEACHING NOTES

In the final mission children are given two pieces of vital information: sweetie beans are sold for £1.25 a bag and that there are 150 beans in each bag.

The orders placed by different shops are either shown as numbers of bags or numbers of beans.

The children must calculate the total cost of each order by either multiplying the number of bags given by £1.25 or by first finding the number of bags for the given number of beans.

Look for children who know and use the fact that 150 goes into 300 twice or derive it by doubling 100 and doubling 50.

Sweetie Bean order

Super Shopper	10 bags
Great Grocers	600 beans
Windy Corner Shop	7 bags
Pukka Prices	12 bags
Tom's Tasty Treats	900 beans

ANSWERS

TM

1) Morning – quarter past eight
   Lunch time – half past twelve
   Afternoon – quarter to five
2) $8\frac{1}{2}$ hours
3) 225 ml each time, so 675 ml in total.

MM

1) $5\frac{1}{4}$ cm line drawn and labelled.
2)

Day 8	Day 9	Day 10	Day 11	Day 12
$5\frac{1}{2}$ cm	9 cm	$12\frac{1}{2}$ cm	16 cm	$19\frac{1}{2}$ cm

3) Day 14

DV FILES

Super Shopper	10 bags	£12.50
Great Grocers	600 beans	£5
Windy Corner Shop	7 bags	£8.75
Pukka Prices	12 bags	£15
Tom's Tasty Treats	900 beans	£7.50

MISSION 1.11 The Mind Boggles!

MATHEMATICAL CONTENT

- Equivalence
- Fractions of a full turn
- Right angles
- Time (minutes, seconds)
- Multiples of 2 and 3
- Multiplication and division

TEACHING NOTES

The Training Mission requires the children to draw upon the equivalence of a half turn and two right-angle turns. They should also recognise that a half turn would result in the swimmer facing the opposite direction.

The mission continues to focus on equivalence, but now with the number of seconds that are equal to one minute. We are told the number of minutes it takes Huxley to swim to the cave but we are also told that Hailey takes 120 seconds longer.

Look for children who recognise that 120 is double 60, so this is equal to 2 minutes.

The time that Hailey reached the cave must then be calculated starting from a time that is written to five minutes, i.e. 20 past 11.

The theme of equivalence continues in this mission as the children are asked to draw on the counting they have done in twos and threes, and, therefore, from some of their multiplication tables.

They are asked to find the number of one type of fish that have an equivalent number of eyes to a number of the other type of fish, e.g.

'How many *three-eyed Boggle Fish* will have the same number of eyes as 15 *two-eyed Boggle Fish?*'

They should use what they know about numbers that appear in both the counts of 2 and the counts of 3 from zero. Some children may recognise these as the numbers in a count of 6 from zero and relate this to the fact that $2 \times 3 = 6$.

The children are then given the opportunity to make up statements of their own drawing from these known facts or ones that have been found. Encourage the children to go beyond 12 fish (as in the example above).

DV FILES

The final problem requires the children to find all possibilities by trying different combinations of Boggle Fish to reach the given total of eyes counted in each of Huxley's photographs.

Look for children who confidently manipulate multiples of 2 and 3 to help find a solution and draw on their findings form the Main Mission.

Again, ways of being systematic should be encouraged if children are finding it difficult to find all solutions or to find a starting place.

The children are also asked to describe any patterns they see. This should be commonplace when children are finding all possibilities as it helps to identify any rules that may govern a set of solutions.

ANSWERS

TM

1) half turn
   2 right angle turns
2) 15 minutes
3) twenty-five to twelve (25 to 12, 11:35)

MM

1) 6
2) 10
3) E.g.

   2 *three-eyed boggle fish* will have the same number of eyes as **3** *two-eyed boggle fish*.

   6 *three-eyed boggle fish* will have the same number of eyes as **9** *two-eyed boggle fish*.

DV FILES

Photograph 1

Photograph 1
30 eyes in total

Two-eyed	Three-eyed	Total eyes
15	0	30 + 0 = 30
12	2	24 + 6 = 30
9	4	18 + 12 = 30
6	6	12 + 18 = 30
3	8	6 + 24 = 30
0	10	0 + 30 = 30

Two-eyed Boggle Fish 15, 12, 9 etc. going down in threes, but three-eyed Boggle Fish 0, 2, 4, 6 etc. going up in twos.

Photograph 2

Photograph 2
39 eyes in total

Two-eyed	Three-eyed	Total eyes
18	1	36 + 3 = 39
15	3	30 + 9 = 39
12	5	24 + 15 = 39
9	7	18 + 21 = 39
6	9	12 + 27 = 39
3	11	6 + 33 = 39
0	13	0 + 39 = 39

Two-eyed Boggle Fish going down in threes, but three-eyed Boggle Fish going up in twos.

MATHEMATICAL CONTENT

- 2-D shapes
- Fractions of sets or amounts
- Sequences
- Addition and subtraction multiples of 10
- Understanding the =, < and > sign
- Multiples of 5 and 10

TEACHING NOTES

TM The Training Mission requires children to recognise or name 2-D shapes and then describe the number of each as a fraction of the total set. In all cases, the children will need to consider equivalent fractions for $\frac{1}{3}$ and $\frac{1}{4}$.

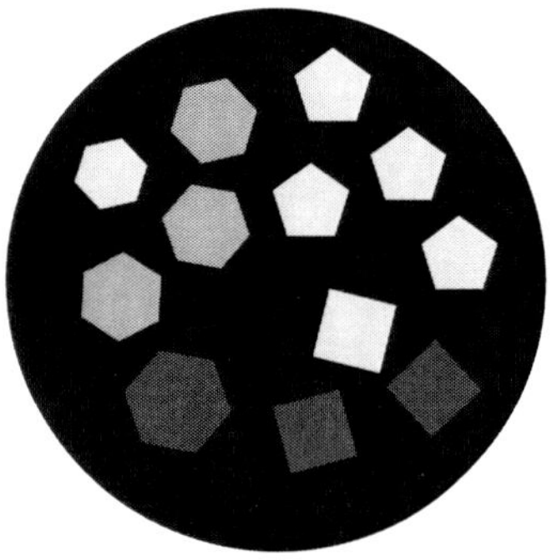

Although all the shapes shown here are familiar representations of the pentagon and hexagon in their regular form, the final question asks the children to name and draw a mystery shape with eight vertices.

Look for children who automatically draw an image of a regular octagon and those that recognise that it could be any closed shape with eight straight sides.

MM A different number of samples are taken from various parts of Ham's space suit. The number of samples follows sequences that increase either by 20, 30 or 40.

Look for children who draw on the knowledge that when a multiple of 10 is either added or subtracted, the number of units or ones stay the same. Children will, of course, find in Key Stage 2 that the pattern does change when zero is crossed.

They should also recognise and be able to explain that the tens digit in each sequence also increases each time in relation to the number added, i.e. increases by 3 when 30 is added, but only increases by 2 when 20 is added.

DV FILES

The number of samples of the mystery shape is determined by two sets of clues.

Children must first recognise that the number of samples they are looking for on the arm will all end in zero as it is a multiple of 10, whereas it can end with a five or zero on the leg as it is a multiple of 5.

They must also refer back to the sequences in the Main Mission to narrow down the range of possibilities.

Here they are required to make sense of statements using the greater than or less than sign.

Encourage them to suggest all possible solutions.

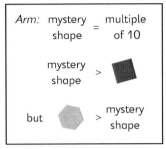

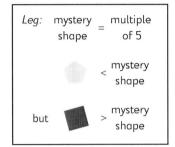

ANSWERS

TM

1) $\frac{1}{3}$
2) $\frac{1}{4}$
3) hexagon
4) octagon, e.g. ⬡ or ⬡

MM

		Head	Arm	Leg	Back	Front
1)		23	43	63	83	103
2)		17	47	77	107	137
3)		29	69	109	149	189

DV FILES

Arm: more than 47 samples but less than 69.

Possible solutions are 50 and 60 as we know it has to be a multiple of 10.

Leg: more than 63 samples but less than 77.

Possible solutions are 65, 70 and 75 as we know it has to be a multiple of 5.

MATHEMATICAL CONTENT

- Odd numbers
- Multiples of 10
- Division
- Distance (metres)

- Addition and subtraction
- Place value
- Number facts (including bonds to 100)
- Sequences

TEACHING NOTES

TM

The mission focuses on the safe transport of three families of ducks to a new pond elsewhere in the village.

The children must first identify the number of ducks that live in these large families. They are told that there are 100 ducks altogether, but then are given clues to help find the exact number in each family.

Children draw on knowledge of number bonds to 100, odd numbers, division and patterns found in numbers that are all one more than a multiple of 10.

A final clue that reveals that there are nearly 30 in one of the families helps the children to identify the solution from the possible set of solutions that they have so far.

MM

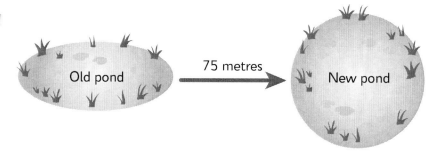

The key facts here are that only two ducks can be carried at a time and 75 m is the distance of a one-way journey to the new pond. Omar and Rosa must always walk a further 75 m each time to return to the old pond to collect the next pair of ducks.

Using knowledge of doubles, children should identify that as Omar has carried twice as many ducks, he must have walked twice as far. The difference is, therefore, 300 m.

Look for children who recognise that all complete journeys are lots of 150 m and can use this to explain why Omar, having walked 800 m, is not yet back at the old pond. He still has 100 m left to go.

DV FILES

To complete the mission, the children must help Rosa find her way around a group of dogs that are out on a walk.

The grid is filled with sets of numbers that create patterns (sequences). In order to avoid the dogs, Rosa must follow suggested patterns to get to the new pond.

The children must identify patterns and provide the rule that they have used.

93	102	?	?	New pond
?	125	150	51	54
75	50	🐕	48	45
66	25	43	39	42
57	Ducks	33	36	44

Several question marks can also be found in the grid so that they can be used in different ways to help complete each sequence.

Look for the strategies children use when adding 9 each time to complete the sequence 57, 66, 75, 84, 93, 102, etc. or any explanations they may use for simply continuing the pattern of ascending tens and descending units or ones until zero is reached (12**0** in this case).

ANSWERS

TM

1)

A	11	21	31	41	51	61	71
B	69	59	49	39	29	19	9
C	20	20	20	20	20	20	20

2) The number of ducks in Family B all have 9 units or ones. The 9 must go with the 1 from Family A to make another ten as the total needed (80) is a multiple of 10.

3) 29 Family B so Family A must be 51.

MM

1) 300 m
2) 300 m
3) It takes 150 m to go to the new pond and back. We know that 600 m is walked for eight ducks, another 150 m for another two ducks and then only 50 m is left to make up 800 m. This is not enough to get to the new pond and back again.

Children may also explain that, after 600 m, the next time Omar is back at the old post is after 750 m and then after 900 m so he could not be back there after 800 m.

DV FILES

Route 1: Add 3 each time or multiples of 3
33, 36, 39, 42, 45, 48, 51, 54

Route 2: Add 25 each time or multiples of 25
25, 50, 75, 100, 125, 150, 175, 200

Route 3: Add 9 each time
57, 66, 75, 84, 93, 102, 111, 120

MATHEMATICAL CONTENT

- Money
- Addition and subtraction
- Multiplication (including doubles)
- Place value
- Partitioning
- Length (cm)

TEACHING NOTES

 The children must initially prove or disprove the statement made by Babs about where best to buy the two items they want for Da Vinci's birthday presents. Children may provide worked examples to show that the total is the same at each store or simply explain the 25p differences.

The problem develops to consider change from £30 when both items are purchased from *PC Prices* and the change they will get if they decide to choose the cheaper option and buy the case from *Tablet Things* and the charger from *PC Prices*.

 In the search for some screen wipes on different internet sites, the children must help the team decide where best to buy the required 30 wipes.

Wipes are advertised in different quantities, e.g. 5 wipes and 10 wipes, 10 wipes and 20 wipes.

Children must use the information to reason about the best value for money for each of the online sites. They should draw on knowledge of doubling and multiples of 5 or 10 that total 30.

Look for children who use multiplication and those that use repeated addition to calculate. The children must then investigate all the different ways of buying 30 wipes at *On the Web*.

They should be encouraged to find all possibilities.

With all the information, the Brain Academy team are helped to finally decide where *and how* it is cheaper to buy the 30 wipes.

DV FILES

The presents need wrapping. Three pieces of wrapping paper are suggested to wrap the case.

All dimensions are provided in centimetres and Huxley's Helpline provides the reminder that there must be no gaps in the paper so it should be a bit bigger.

The key to this problem is remembering than the case (or wrapping paper) can be turned around and that it does need to cover both sides of the present. Children should reason that the length of either side of the case can be doubled to find a potential piece, but it is not necessary to double both sides.

Look for the strategies used to double numbers, e.g. partitioning 17 into 10 and 7 first.

Which doubles do the children already know and recall without the need to calculate?

Once the suitable piece (C) has been identified, the children are required to explain why the other two pieces were not able to be used.

ANSWERS

1) E.g. 'No, because £7 + £15 = £22 and £6.75 + £15.25 is also £22.'

   Or 'No, because the charger is 25p less at PC Online but the case is 25p more, so it works out the same.'

2) £8

3) They should buy the charger from PC Prices and the case from Tablet Things.

   This will cost £6.75 + £15 = £21.75.

4) £8.25

PC Online	
10 wipes	£3.50
20 wipes	£6.75

ON THE WEB	
5 wipes	£1.70
10 wipes	£3.95

1) 10 wipes plus 20 wipes is £3.50 + £6.75 = £10.25

   10 wipes × 3 is £3.50 × 3 (or £3.50 + £3.50 + £3.50) = £10.50

2)

5 wipes £1.70	10 wipes £3.95	Total for 30 wipes
0	3	£3.95 × 3 = £11.85
2	2	£1.70 + £1.70 + £3.95 + £3.95 or use doubles = £11.30
4	1	£1.70 + £1.70 + £1.70 + £1.70 + £3.95 or use doubles etc. = £10.75
6	0	£1.70 × 6 = £10.20

3) Buy 6 lots of 5 wipes from *On the Web*.

DV FILES

1) E.g. Paper C is the best because 2 × 17 cm is 34 cm, so there is 3 cm left over. The case is 26 cm long and the paper is 28 cm, so there is 2 cm left over.

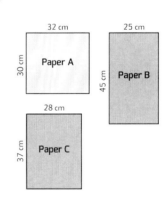

2) Explanations to show that:
   - Paper A will not work because 32 cm is less than the 34 cm needed (or 52 cm needed for double 26 cm) even though 30 cm is plenty for the 26 cm length.
   - Paper B is longer but narrower. There is plenty for the 34 cm needed but the length of the case is 26 cm and the paper is only 25 cm wide.

MISSION 1.15 Dear Da Vinci Diary

MATHEMATICAL CONTENT

- Time (hours, minutes, days and months)
- Calculating time intervals
- Addition and subtraction
- Calendars

TEACHING NOTES

The mission begins with the children suggesting possible times for team meetings for the remaining days of the week. We are told that they are later than *half past 8* but earlier than *half past 10*. No meetings are at the same time.

Look for children who recognise that a range of different times are possible and can include times like 10 past 9 in addition to the o'clock, half past/to and quarter past/to times already given.

Children are required to reason about the time that Huxley has left to re-charge the battery before Da Vinci's video call. From the answers to Question 2, we already know when the battery is put on to charge, so explanations should prove that there is not sufficient time before the video call.

Huxley is planning the number of team meetings needed across a year.

Children should make use of Huxley's own verse to help identify the number of meetings needed each month.

You may even choose to cover the verse initially as children may know their own version or this would be a useful assessment opportunity.

The months are grouped in threes, so totals must be found. Children should reason and explain why the total for January, February and March is 91 rather than 90. They should recognise that February must have an extra day so it is a leap year.

DV FILES

This mission requires children to use what they know about calendars to help them make a decision.

The calendar for April has not been given, so look for the ways that children find or calculate the number of Wednesdays in this month. Do they write out the rest of the calendar for March and then April filling in all the days, or add seven each time to just find the dates of all Wednesdays?

The children should prove that it is not possible as there are only four Wednesdays in March and another four in April. This is only eight altogether.

You may want to extend the problem a bit further to ask children to investigate or explain if it is ever possible, e.g. *sometimes true, always true, never true* type problems. It would be possible if the month of March began on a Monday, Tuesday or Wednesday.

ANSWERS

TM

1) Any times after 8:30 a.m. but before 10:30 a.m., but not 9 o'clock, 9:45 a.m. or 10:15 p.m.

   E.g. quarter to 9, quarter past nine and half past 9 (or twenty to 9 etc.)

2) Tuesday – quarter to 1.

   Wednesday – quarter past 12.

3) No, because there is only $\frac{3}{4}$ hour between being put on charge at quarter past 12 and 1 o'clock when the video call begins. The call should not begin until quarter past 1.

MM

1)

Months grouped in threes			Total
January	February	March	91
April	May	June	91
July	August	September	92
October	November	December	92

2) It must be a leap year as 31 + 28 + 31 = 90 days, so February has 29 days in the year shown here.

DV FILES

March

M	T	W	Th	F	Sa	Su
			1	2	3	4
5	6	7	8	9	10	11
12	13	14	15	16	17	18
19	20	21	22	23	24	25
26	27	28	29	30	31	

April

M	T	W	Th	F	Sa	Su
1	2	3	4	5	6	7
8	9	10	11	12	13	14
15	16	17	18	19	20	21
22	23	24	25	26	27	28
29	30					

Huxley has made a mistake because there will only be four Wednesdays in March this year and four in April.

MISSION 1.16 'Mending' the Law?!

MATHEMATICAL CONTENT

- Fractions of sets or amounts (including equivalent fractions)
- Combining halves and quarters
- Counting in halves and quarters
- Division
- Capacity (ml)
- Subtraction

TEACHING NOTES

The children need to apply their knowledge of fractions to a context that requires them to think initially about 2 out of 6, i.e. two steps out of six are broken. The fraction $\frac{2}{6}$ should then be shown in its simplest form using knowledge of equivalence.

The problem develops as we find out that the same fraction of steps is broken on the medium ladder and on the large one. The number of broken steps is given, but the children need to find out the number of steps there should be in total on each of these ladders.

To find a solution, equivalent fractions should be explored. The key is to recognise that the denominator will give the number of steps in total using the previous language, say *'Four steps out of ... are broken'*. Children may decide to use cubes or sketch ideas to help find a solution.

The Brain Academy team find a box with lots of different pieces of hosepipe. They are either $\frac{1}{4}$ or $\frac{1}{2}$ of a whole pipe. The children must help the team to join them together to make whole pipes again.

The mission builds on children's fluency with counting in fraction steps and recognising how fractions combine to equal one whole or another fraction, e.g. two quarters equal one half.

The problem requires counting beyond one as they must piece together sections to make two or three whole pipes. There is also an element of finding different possibilities as they must find two different solutions for one whole pipe and two whole pipes.

Look for children's recording when finding different possibilities. Do they draw jumps on a number line to show that fractions are numbers in their own right? This may be particularly relevant for Question 2.

Resources, such as integer bars or Cuisenaire Rods, will also support here.

TEACHING NOTES

DV FILES

The final mission focuses on division and the context of capacity.

Firstly, children are required to calculate 56 divided by 4. Look for children who also describe this as a quarter of 56, and perhaps use a method of halving and halving again.

Fraction bars will support this concept.

56			

28	28

14	14	14	14

An image of a jug with a labelled scale provides the necessary information to find out how much water each of the four team members drank. We are told that they each drank the same amount and that 250 ml are left in the jug.

A two-step calculation is needed to subtract 250 ml from the 850 ml and then divide this answer by 4.

ANSWERS

TM

1) $\frac{1}{3}$

2) Medium ladder: 12 steps in total   ($\frac{4}{12}$)
   Tall ladder: 18 steps in total   ($\frac{6}{18}$)

MM

1) E.g.

$\frac{1}{2}$ of whole pipe pieces	$\frac{1}{4}$ of whole pipe pieces	Whole hose pipes
2	0	1
0	4	1
2	4	2
3	2	2
4	4	3

2) $3\frac{1}{2}$ or $3\frac{2}{4}$

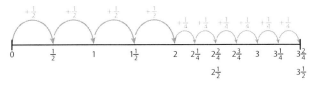

DV FILES

1) 14 in each box.

2) 150 ml.

MISSION 1.17 Build it up!

MATHEMATICAL CONTENT

- 3-D shapes
- Counting in steps of 3 and 5
- Multiplication (including doubling)
- Division

- Length (m and cm)
- Addition and subtraction
- Fractions

TEACHING NOTES

Mason has designed three new buildings. The children must first identify the solid shapes and use the properties of the triangular prism to calculate the number of rectangular faces six of these building will have. Look for children who count in threes, recall facts or use other methods of multiplication, e.g. knowing or counting three threes, then doubling it for six threes.

The problem then considers the number of windows of these six triangular prism-shaped buildings.

Children must remember that there are three rectangular faces, each with five windows, so there are 15 on one building.

Look for children's methods of calculating 15 × 6, e.g. by partitioning into 10 × 6 and 5 × 6. Also look for those that use more simple counting strategies, e.g. counting in fives around the six buildings.

Information is provided regarding the number of steps there are in total and that there are an equal number between floors.

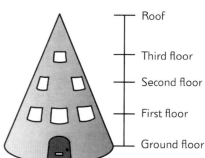

Look for children who mistakenly divide 96 by 4 to find the number of steps between floors, rather than dividing by 3.

This information is then used to find the total number of steps taken to go from the ground floor to the second or to the first floor and back again. Children should recognise this as being the same.

The final question requires calculating 23 m 50 cm x 3 to find the total length of handrail required. Again, look for methods of partitioning and knowledge of 100 centimetres in a metre.

DV FILES

The children are given a set of clues to solve this logic problem. With all problem-solving activities, children should consider the problem as a whole before deciding on a starting point.

The clues are not in the most useful order, so children should reason about which is the most or least important and why.

In this case the cost of the doors is not really needed until the end, but knowing that there are 12 main doors on the second floor is the key information that affects all other clues.

- The ground floor has 20 more main doors than the third floor.
- Doors cost £100 each.
- There are 12 main doors on the second floor.
- The third floor has $\frac{3}{4}$ of the number of main doors as the second floor.
- The first floor has double the number of main doors as third floor.

ANSWERS

TM

1) Building A is a cone, Building B is a triangular prism and Building C is a cylinder.
2) There are 3 rectangular faces on a triangular prism so 18 will be needed for 6 buildings.
3) 5 windows × 3 = 15 windows for each building so 15 × 6 = 90 windows for all 6 buildings.

MM

1) 64 steps
2) 64 steps
3) $23\frac{1}{2}$ m × 3 = 70 m 50 cm

DV FILES

The clues are required in this order, with 3 and 4 being interchangeable:

1. There are 12 main doors on the second floor.
2. The third floor has $\frac{3}{4}$ of the number of main doors as the second floor.
3. The ground floor has 20 more main doors than the third floor.
4. The first floor has double the number of main doors as third floor.
5. Doors cost £100 each.

Ground floor	First floor	Second floor	Third floor	Total
29	18	12	9	68

68 doors × £100 = £6800

MATHEMATICAL CONTENT

- Statistics (pictograms and tally charts)
- Counting in steps of 30 (building on steps of 3 and place value)
- Addition and subtraction
- Mass (kg)

- Multiplication (including doubling) and division (including halving)
- Time (minutes)
- Measurement (km)
- 2-D shapes

TEACHING NOTES

TM

The information about the number of sausages eaten by the children of Sausage City is displayed in a pictogram. The scale is not yet known until the value of one sausage can be determined.

Using the comment made by Huxley, the children should compare the number of Sizzle Sausages and Spicy Sausage eaten. They should reason about the symbols on the pictogram and that the value of one sausage must be the difference of 30 that Huxley has described.

Further questions require the children to prove that a number of a particular variety are eaten and also find the total of two other varieties.

Look for children who draw on knowledge of counting in steps of 3 and apply place value to support counting in steps of 30. Also look for those who can recall 15 as being half of 30 or use an efficient strategy to halve 30, e.g. partitioning.

MM

An incomplete tally chart tells us about the number of 2 kg bags of each fruit that will be delivered to a school. The missing information should be found using knowledge of doubling, multiplication facts or counting in twos.

The children are also required to find the total mass of fruit delivered to each school. Look for children who use number bonds to add 36 kg + 24 kg first.

The final question can be solved in several ways. Look for those who use the longer method of calculating the number of bags of apples delivered to all five school and then subtracting (or finding the difference) between the total number of bags of bananas. A more efficient method is to recognise that four more bags of apples are delivered to each school, so the calculation is simply 4 × 5.

DV FILES

The key here is recognising that the route is a pentagon (regular) so a journey between two schools is always 15 km. Also the children must remember to include the first journey of 15 minutes from the base to Sausage School.

They must find out if all deliveries are made in time for morning break. Children are encouraged to show their findings, so look out for the use of a number line.

A comparison between a 15 km journey and the 10 km journey back to base must be made. Look for those who not only describe the journey as 5 km shorter but also as $\frac{2}{3}$ of 15 km.

They must use what they know about the length of time it takes to drive 15 km (30 minutes) to find that 5 km takes 10 minutes. The time taken to drive 10 km can easily be found. However, children must remember that the solution is not complete as they must add the 20 minutes on to quarter past 10 to find the time the team get back to base.

ANSWERS

TM

1) 30 sausages
2) E.g. Spicy Sausage has 2 lots of 30 sausages and 15 more sausages.

   2 lots of 30 = 60 and then add 15 more equals 75 sausages.
3) 5 × 30 sausages = 150 sausages

   or 30 + 30 + 30 + 30 + 30 = 150 sausages

MM

1)

	Bags of fruit	Total in kg
Apples	卌 卌 IIII	28 kg
Bananas	卌 卌 卌 III	36 kg
Pears	卌 卌 II	24 kg

2) 88 kg
3) Each delivery has 4 more bags of bananas.

   5 × 4 extra bags of bananas = 20 bags
   or 5 schools, so 5 lots of 14 bags of apples and 5 lots of 18 bags of bananas.

DV FILES

1) Children could use number lines, tables, other jottings to show that they finish deliveries at quarter past 10, e.g.

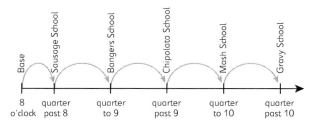

2) Quarter to 10.
3) 25 minutes to 11.

   There are 3 lots of 5 km in 15 km. We know that 15 km takes 30 minutes so each 5 km takes 10 minutes.

   So 10 km, which is 2 lots of 5 km, will take 20 minutes.

   Or, 10 km is $\frac{2}{3}$ of 15 km so find $\frac{2}{3}$ of 30 minutes.

CURRICULUM MATCHING CHART

Each Brain Academy mission covers a range of mathematical topics and requires children to make connections between areas of mathematics. The chart below shows which areas of the 2014 National Curriculum Programme of Study for Mathematics are covered in each mission.

Domain		Mission 1.1	1.2	1.3	1.4	1.5	1.6
NUMBER	Place value		✔	✔		✔	✔
	Estimating						
	Addition and subtraction	✔			✔	✔	
	Multiplication and division	✔		✔	✔	✔	
	Fractions			✔			
MEASUREMENT	Length	✔		✔	✔	✔	
	Mass/Weight				✔		
	Volume/Capacity				✔		
	Temperature		✔				
	Time		✔				
	Money						
GEOMETRY	Properties of shape	✔				✔	✔
	2-D shapes	✔				✔	
	3-D shapes						✔
	Position and direction			✔			✔
DATA	Venn diagrams						✔
	Bar charts						
	Pictograms and tally charts						

Mission											
1.7	1.8	1.9	1.10	1.11	1.12	1.13	1.14	1.15	1.16	1.17	1.18
✔					✔	✔	✔				✔
			✔					✔			
✔	✔	✔			✔	✔	✔	✔	✔	✔	✔
✔		✔		✔	✔	✔	✔		✔	✔	✔
		✔			✔				✔	✔	
✔			✔			✔	✔			✔	✔
		✔									✔
			✔						✔		
✔			✔	✔				✔			✔
			✔				✔				
					✔					✔	
					✔						
										✔	
✔				✔							
	✔										
											✔

National Association for Able Children in Education

What is NACE?

NACE, a registered charity founded in 1983, is the leading independent organisation for the education of the more able.

What does NACE do?

NACE specialises in working with teachers and schools to improve learning for the more able and to turn ability into achievement for all.

The NACE community provides teachers with:
A members' website including:
·   Guidance and resources
·   New to A,G&T
·   Subject specific resources
·   Specialist advice
·   An award winning monthly E-bulletin packed with sources of inspiration and
    regular updates
·   NACE Insight, a termly newsletter

How will the book help me?

The *Brain Academy* Maths Mission Files challenge and help you to become better at learning and a better mathematician by:
·   thinking of and testing different solutions to problems
·   making connections to what you already know
·   working by yourself and with others
·   expecting you to get better and to go on to the next book
·   learning skills which you can use in other subjects and out of school.

We hope you enjoy the books!